The Old Fashioned Hand-Writing Book

The no-nonsense hand-writing book to help you practise a writing style

**Ward Lock Educational
47 Marylebone Lane
London W1M 6AX**

Other titles in this series:

The Old Fashioned Times Table Book
ISBN 0 7062 3749 8

The Old Fashioned Adding-Up Book
ISBN 0 7062 4086 3

The Old Fashioned Rules of Grammar Book
ISBN 0 7062 3850 8

The Old Fashioned Rules of Spelling Book
ISBN 0 7062 4085 5

First published 1981

Printed by Williamson Printing Ltd.
Davis Road, Chessington, Surrey KT9 1TT
for Ward Lock Educational
47 Marylebone Lane
London W1M 6AX
A Ling Kee Company

ISBN 0 7062 4139 8
Made in Great Britain

YOUR WRITING ALPHABET   The best way
to learn the letters of the alphabet is in
family groups of similar movement.

i t l ∩ n m r h b p k

u u y ɢ o c a d g q e

v v w c f j s x x z

Here are some basic rules to enable you
to write clearly and quickly.

1. Try to keep all the down strokes level
   with a slight slope to the right.

l ı l ı l ı l h f y l j b p

2. Make the rounded letters egg shaped.

o o o o o c a d g q e

3. Keep the different parts of the letters in
   their correct spaces.

ARMS
    BODY   l o d g e b y
        LEGS

4. Notice how the letters start and end.

→ u p n   → a d g

↳ h e k   → f t w

3

FAMILY GROUPS   These letters require
similar movements. Begin at the dot.
Only five letters have two strokes f i j t x.

i t l i t l i t l i t l

i _____

_____

n m r h n m r h

n _____

_____

b p b p b p b p b

b _____

_____

u y u y u y u y

u _____

_____

o c a d g q e e e e

o _____ e _____

_____

4

v w v w v w v w v w

v _____

_____

f j s f j s f j s f j s

f _____

_____

x x x x z z z z

x _____

_____

Now practise writing letters from different groups. They make interesting patterns. Here are some examples.

n u n u n b q b q b

n _____

h y h y h m o m o m

h _____

g k g k g k a x a x a

g _____

5

These letters start with a point.

1 1 1 1 → *i j m n*

i _____ *i* _____

_____

p r s t u v w x y

p _____

_____

Practise these letters again.

1 1 1 1 → *y x w v*

i _____ *y* _____

_____

u t s p r m n j i

u _____

_____

These letters can start with a rounded stroke if preferred.

1 1 1 1 → *n m r x*

These letters start with a curve.

⌒ ⌒ ⌒ ⌒ ⌒ o c o c o

a d g q *also* s s s s

Now practise the two groups of letters which start with a point and a curved stroke.

1 ⌒ 1 ⌒ 1 ⌒ → i o j c

m a n d p g r q s

o t c u a v d w g

x q y s i o j m a

These letters end with a rounded hook.

ι ι ι ι ι ι → a c d

ι   a

e h i l k m n u x

e

These letters end with a horizontal stroke.

- - - - → f o t v w

• ·····   f

Now practise the letters which end with
a rounded hook and a horizontal stroke.

ι‾ ι‾ ι‾ ι‾ ⇉ a f c o

ι·····   a

d t e v h w i f k

d

o l t m v n w u f

o _____

x o a t c v d w g

x _____

The letter 'e' is the only letter which has
a loop. Begin in the middle of its shape
at the dot.

e e e e e e e e e

e _____

_____

Now write the alphabet in the normal
manner. Try to remember the correct
starting point and movement.

a b c d e f g h i j

a _____

k l m n o p q r s

k _____

t u v w x y z

t _____

DIAGONAL LINK *The next step is to learn how to join your letters together. The most important and frequent link is the diagonal join.*

/ / / / u u u u

/

ai aj am an ap

ai

ar as at au av

ar

aw ax ay

Alternative join: as

aw

Try to keep the diagonal strokes even.

ai / ei / lu / in

di ip en ku cy as

d

um ti nu ep it is

u

av kn iw hu ar ci

a

ly ap us uy im an

l

You can link to the letters m n r x with
a rounded stroke if preferred.

vi vi am an ar ax

vi

When linking to letters with ascenders use
a long pointed join. Make a slight curve.

il il il il ab af ah

il _____

_____

ak al eb nf ch lk

ak _____

_____

el kl uf ih ef cl il

el _____

_____

mb th ik ul ib lf

mb _____

_____

Treat the letter 't' like a short ascender.

at ht it nt et lt ct

at _____

The forward and backward join is used
when linking to the rounded letters.

ư   ư   ư   aa   ac   ad

ư

ag   aơ   aq   *Alternative link
to letter 's':* as

ag

ha   uq   na   ld   tơ   ig

ha

ac   kơ   ca   dơ   eq   as

ac

hơ   ns   ic   ed   ag   ma

hơ

*Reminder: Are you keeping all the down
strokes the same slope and the diagonal
strokes at the same angle?*

| ı | ı | ı | ı | ı | ı | ı | / | / | / | / | /

Joining to a letter 'e'

ee de ie ne le te ce

e

me he ee ue ae ke

m

HORIZONTAL LINK *This link is not used so frequently as a diagonal join. Linking to a pointed letter:*

ι ι ι ι fi oi ti vi

ι fi

wi fr op tw vu wi

w

A diagonal link can be used when you join from the letter 't' if preferred. th ti tn

14

ৰ ৰ ৰ ৰ *fl ob th vt*

ৰ

wh *ft ok th vl wh*

wh

Linking to rounded letters

τ τ τ τ *fa oo ta vs*

τ

wa fa oa ta va wd

wa

fs od ta vo ws oq

fs

When a letter 'e' follows a horizontal stroke it is best at first to leave it unjoined. This also includes the letter 'r'.

fe oe te ve we re

f _____

_____

As you learn to write quickly most letters will become joined, but when you first practise writing words do not join from these letters.

b g j p q r s x y z

b _____

Here are some examples of words using these letters.

boy sun pop are joy

b _____

exit zoom quiz buy

e _____

age yell growl run

a _____

Now write the alphabet linking the letters with the correct joins. Do not join from the letters with a dot.

abcdefg hij klmnop

a _____

qrstuvwxyz

q _____

When learning to write words you can, if you wish, slightly change the shape of a few letters. This way you do not have so many pen strokes, and linking will be easier. The letters are:

b v w p x z r

b _____

Here are some examples of words using these letters.

boy won vows pane

b _____

excit dozen run bows

e _____

Now try writing these flowing exercises and words. Write them slowly, carefully and correctly, and then gradually try to increase your speed of writing. Do not join from the letters with a dot.

hm uuu hm uuu

hum in mum nun

lululul tititi lululul

ill lit till lull hill

vwvw vur wowo

wavy towel woven

cccc cow cave cook

Now try some more.

db db db db db db

d _____

body bid bead bad

b _____

dp dp dp dp dp dp

d _____

dip drop dump pod

d _____

hy eeeee hy eeeee hy

h _____

heel yell meets hay

h _____

olololol fafafafa

o _____

flow loop fall loaf

f _____

19

Now practise some words.

they and our many

what can my every

sun age hot each he

like shall you plays

was from come going

fly own toy bit girl

like boy cool we but

run stop go laugh is

Practise some words of your own choice.

_____

_____

_____

_____

_____

_____

_____

Write your name.

_____

_____

Now write your address.

_____

_____

_____

CAPITAL LETTERS *These letters are chiefly used to indicate the beginning of sentences, names and headings. Keep your capitals a little shorter in height than the 'arms' or ascenders of the small letters.* → Hh

● OQCGUD

■ HAVNTXYZK

■ ILEFPBRSJ

■ MW

Numbers

1 2 3 4 5 6 7 8 9 0

More words with capitals and small letters for you to practise.

Week Days   Monday

STOP GO THIS WAY

Tuesday Wednesday

← EXIT ENTRANCE →

Thursday Friday

LOOK-AND-LISTEN

Saturday & Sunday

SOME FINAL HINTS

Always leave a border of space around the text.

Allow enough space between lines of writing to clear the 'arms' and 'legs'. Three 'o' spaces is a good measure.

Keep an eye on your word spacing. One letter space is ideal.

Hold your writing tool very lightly and keep your fingers about 2 cms. from the point.

Right handers: Place your paper in the position as shown in the picture.

Left handers: Place your paper in the position as shown in the picture.